POISONOUS FUNGI

POISONOUS FUNGI

By

JOHN RAMSBOTTOM
Keeper of Botany
British Museum (Natural History)

With Colour Plates

by

ROSE ELLENBY

The KING PENGUIN *Books*
PUBLISHED BY PENGUIN BOOKS LIMITED
LONDON *and* NEW YORK
1945

THE KING PENGUIN BOOKS
Editor : N. B. L. Pevsner
Technical Editor : R. B. Fishenden

MADE IN GREAT BRITAIN

Text Pages printed by
R. & R. CLARK, LTD., EDINBURGH
Set in Monotype Bembo

Colour Plates
Made & Printed by JOHN SWAIN & SON, LTD.

Cover design by
JOY JARVIS

PUBLISHED BY

PENGUIN BOOKS LIMITED
HARMONDSWORTH MIDDLESEX
ENGLAND

PENGUIN BOOKS INC.
245 FIFTH AVENUE
NEW YORK

POISONOUS FUNGI

For Mary (Fungi officio, 1939–1945)

DOUBTLESS so soon as man learned by experience that fungi could serve as food he found also that some were poisonous. It is not therefore surprising that the first mention we have of fungi refers to this; when the poet Euripides (480–406 B.C.) was at Icarus a woman with two grown-up sons and a married daughter ate fungi gathered from the fields and were 'destroyed by pitiless fate in one day'. There are repeated references to poisoning in classical writings, and this may give the impression that fungi were regarded as forbidden fruit. Indeed Pliny's query, 'What great pleasure then can there be in partaking of a dish of so doubtful a character as this?' has often been quoted in support of this view: he was, however, warning against Suillus (*Boletus edulis*) which was very conveniently adapted for administering poisons, by which whole families and guests had recently been removed. If fungi had not been commonly eaten, why the frequent warnings? Many rich Romans valued them so highly that they employed special collectors. Among these patrons was Caesar Claudius poisoned by his wife Agrippina, who 'offered unto him a mushroom empoisoned knowing that he was most greedy of such meats'. He 'descended into heaven' and his stepson Nero called fungi 'the food of the gods' in reference to Claudius's deifications, an irregular one at Colchester and the normal one at death. The mushroom was doubtless *Amanita caesarea*, much prized on the Continent but absent from this country. To many the very word fungus suggests something mysterious, something morbid. Some of the early herbalists seeking a derivation for the word found it in *funus* (a funeral) and *ago* (to put in motion):

John Ray while doubting its correctness considered it appropriate. *Amanita caesarea* is one of the few species that can be recognised with certainty from the old descriptions. It was comparatively easy to describe herbs, shrubs and trees clearly enough for them to be recognised; indeed many of the old names are still used. But toadstools are for the most part short-lived and irregular in occurrence and their distinguishing characters are not very easy to grasp. Consequently, instead of clear descriptions of those species which were known to be safe and those which are dangerous, various rules were given for distinguishing the two groups. These rules were repeated by the herbalists and many of them have a world-wide currency even today. The primary division into edible and poisonous species influenced the classification of fungi until comparatively recent times.

With the gradual recognition of the essential characters for distinguishing species a more exact knowledge of the gastronomic qualities of fungi was attained. As a result we know that all rule-of-thumb methods for differentiating between edible and poisonous species are without the slightest value and, further, despite popular belief, the number of poisonous fungi is not legion but is very small: the plates in this booklet have had to be eked out with edible fungi! The title 'Poisonous Fungi' is therefore somewhat misleading except in so far that all have been described as such sometime or other. With the realisation that most fleshy fungi are non-poisonous there is difficulty in defining the common terms mushroom and toadstool. So long as only the Field Mushroom with, at most, one or two of its near relatives were regarded as edible, it was easy to define a mushroom as an edible fungus and a toadstool as a poisonous one, as indeed is customary. If, however, edibility is the criterion we have in this country hundreds of mushrooms and possibly a dozen toadstools, which completely reverses the picture.

According to the Oxford English Dictionary both terms were originally applied indiscriminately to all umbrella-shaped fungi: the main definition of toadstool reads: 'A fungus having a round disk-like top and a slender stalk, a mushroom'. It would be well to return to this original use of toadstool and retain mushroom, so far as possible, in its usually accepted sense as a member of the genus *Psalliota*, i.e. for the Field Mushroom, Horse Mushroom and their near relatives. The word mushroom has a long history with numerous spellings: in the fifteenth century we find musseroun and muscheron. It is presumably the old French *moisseron* (*mousseron*) derived from *mousse*, moss. The word toadstool has an even longer history, appearing as tadstole and tode stole in the fourteenth century; todyshatte is an interesting variant. The derivation is the obvious one: we have paddoc-stol (paddock-stool) in the fifteenth century which recalls the modern Dutch *paddestoel*.

Although since the outbreak of war many people in this country have reconsidered their opinions about edible fungi, the majority still believe that only the Cultivated Mushroom is to be trusted. The Pauline 'Whatsoever is sold in the shambles, that eat, asking no question' is religiously adopted. Two points, however, need passing attention though they are common to all foods. Fungi should be eaten fresh, for as they age they may undergo change of themselves or, more likely, be acted upon by other organisms including moulds and bacteria and may be rendered harmful. The practice in many London shops of exposing mushrooms for sale so long as they retain their shape should be forbidden.

The second point concerns personal idiosyncrasy or allergy. Just as some people cannot without discomfort partake of certain proteid-containing food such as milk, butter, eggs, honey, tomatoes, strawberries, fish, so some are made ill by the smallest portion of a fungus which is perfectly harmless to others. The idiosyncrasy varies: a particular species only may cause trouble, or it may be many, or all. Occasionally a drop of mushroom ketchup has an effect out of all proportion to the amount of fungus absorbed. The phenomenon is not more frequent with fungi than with several common foods, but its manifestation usually creates more alarm, particularly if perchance there is not that psychological sense of safety which purchase bestows. Fungi as a whole are somewhat indigestible and consequently a certain discretion is advisable concerning the time and the amount of the meal by those needing to pay attention to such matters. There are, however, some species which are especially indigestible. One noteworthy example is the Yellow Staining Mushroom (*Psalliota xanthoderma*, Pl. 12). Some other species figured are also very indigestible, though the gastro-intestinal effects they produce in some people may be due to definite resinoid substances which act on the mucous lining of the intestine. This is certainly so with *Entoloma lividum* (Pl. 9) where the symptoms are very severe and may be fatal.

Several species which cause purging were formerly held in high esteem. The most celebrated was 'Agarick' (*Polyporus officinalis*) which was regarded as a panacea and is still on sale as White, or Purging Agaric. The other poisonous species may be classified as:

1. Those containing substances which after a long incubation period bring about the degeneration of the cells of the body: *Amanita phalloides* (Pl. 1), *Amanita verna* and *Amanita virosa* (Pl. 2) are deadly. The rare *Lepiota helveola* (Pl. 6) belongs to this group but is much less dangerous.

2. Those containing substances which paralyse the nervous system: *Amanita muscaria* (Pl. 4), *Amanita pantherina* (Pl. 5) and *Inocybe Patouillardi* (Pl. 11).

3. Those containing substances which destroy the red blood corpuscles: *Gyromitra esculenta* (Pl. 16).

For convenience of reference the details of symptoms are given with the descriptions of the several species.

Although all British toadstools known definitely to be poisonous are described and illustrated it should not be assumed that the remainder can be eaten with impunity, if not always with relish, for obviously large numbers have not been sampled, even excluding those having insufficient substance or too much tenacity to be of culinary interest. Indeed there is evidence that a few other species have caused illness, but sometimes this has followed the consumption of uncooked specimens or there is some other factor of uncertainty. Though abroad some toadstools are eaten raw in salads it is not a practice to follow without proper consideration, for some fungi which are perfectly safe when cooked are discomforting when not.

If the descriptions and the accompanying plates are studied, the poisonous species will be found to have no structural or other character in common. Despite popular belief to the contrary, there is only one practical way of distinguishing between edible and poisonous toadstools. This experimental method is sure, but the result may not profit a man. Moreover it is unnecessary, for we have the data from many unvolitional trials. Among those who thus contributed to our knowledge were many exalted personages whose names are immortalised in mycological writings. Pope Clement VII and Emperor Charles VI are always included, though apparently without warrant: the latter was so fond of fungi that he forbade their use in his States lest there should be a shortage.

As with other foods the only safe method to follow is to rely on the experience of one's predecessors. There are many toadstools which are perfectly wholesome and readily distinguished. Indiscriminate eating of others may render the consumer meet for repentance or beyond it.

An expression frequently used is that certain toadstools 'look poisonous'. This usually refers to colour, though sometimes it is shape or structure. Bright colours are most often supposed to be danger signals, but all colours except white, cream or pale yellow arouse suspicion. Colour, however, is of no significance of itself in determining whether a fungus is poisonous or not: its importance lies in its being one of the main characters which distinguish one species from another. Similarly with shape and structure. The Field Mushroom is presumably taken as the model by which all other species are judged, so the more a fungus differs from this pattern the more likely is it thought to deviate from perfection as food. Moreover the doctrine of signatures still has its hold and a fungus with a fancied resemblance to something unpleasant is assumed to be itself objectionable. Whatever the shape or structure of a toadstool, whatever it reminds one of, are not of the slightest value in determining whether it is wholesome.

Many fungi have characteristic smells which to an experienced collector serve as an aid to identification. Smells are very difficult to define. People differ in their sensitiveness and in their criteria of association. A scent may be pleasing to one, intolerable to another, and undetected by a third apart from any difference in general olfactory sensibility. We have no means of defining scent except by comparison, and as this is not usually made directly but from memory there may be considerable variety in describing that of a given fungus.

There is a great range of odours among toadstools. That of the Field Mushroom is sufficiently marked to be characterised for purposes of comparison as a mushroom smell, the commonest met with. Many species have the odour of new meal; a few smell of rancid meal. Several have the sweet smell of anise. Many species have scents resembling that of fruits; others suggest flowers—jasmine, hyacinth, musk; many smell of garlic; several have a radishy smell. And so on—fish, crab, goat-moth, coal-gas, ammonia, prussic acid, acetylene. Several species have the offensive smell of bed-bugs and, less commonly, stronger terms than scent, smell and odour are called for, with occasional allusions not usually considered proper.

Most frequently a good sniff is needed to detect what odour there is; sometimes, however, it is noticeable anywhere in the neighbourhood of the fungus; occasionally it is necessary to bruise or cut a specimen for it to become manifest. Dried specimens often retain their special odour for many years.

It might be thought that smell would give a clue to edibility, but unfortunately this is not so. None of the British poisonous species has an unpleasant smell and the deadly poisonous species of *Amanita* are odourless.

It has been a common belief from earliest times that if the flesh of a fungus changes colour when cut or broken, it is poisonous. Some species of *Boletus*, e.g. *Boletus luridus*, almost instantly become a vivid blue when broken; other fungi become reddish, yellowish or blackish and the 'milk' of some species of *Lactarius* gradually changes colour. None of these colour changes is of any significance in denoting the presence of poisonous substances. The bright blues are doubtless disconcerting when preparing a fungus for cooking but they are not danger signals. The Field Mushroom (*Psalliota campestris*) and the Horse Mushroom (*Psalliota arvensis*) change colour slightly, the flesh of the first becoming slightly reddish, that of the second yellowish: other mushrooms show a stronger coloration, red in *Psalliota haemorrhoidaria*, yellow in the Yellow Staining Mushroom (*Psalliota xanthoderma*, Pl. 12).

The change of colour is a chemical phenomenon. Certain substances, which because of their properties are called chromogens (e.g. boletol in *Boletus* spp.; tyrosin in *Russula* spp.), occur in the flesh together with oxydising exzymes (laccase, tyrosinase) which act upon them in the presence of oxygen and moisture and as a result the chromogens acquire a new, sometimes a vivid colour. On continued contact with air the flesh may undergo a series of colour changes due to a gradual alteration in the chromogen.

The most widely current belief is that edible fungi 'peel'. This relic of antiquity is relied on by many to distinguish the Field Mushroom from all other species. Whether the skin of the cap can be removed or not depends upon a structural character. If the epidermis is formed of two different kinds of tissue so that there are two distinct layers, the outer skin can be removed; if it is in one layer, it is too closely applied to the underlying tissue to come away without tearing. Members of the same genus may differ in this respect: thus *Russula emetica* has a separable pellicle whereas *Russula drimeia* has not (Pl. 8). Whether or not a fungus will peel is a character of a species, but it gives no clue to edibility. The Field Mushroom peels, but so does the Death Cap. A failure to realise this led to two deaths at Ipswich last year (1944).

Almost equally current is the similarly antique belief that a poisonous fungus is revealed in cooking if a silver spoon is turned black, though probably it is rarely tried. Silver is blackened by sulphides but presumably is not affected by any fungus, certainly not by *Amanita phalloides*. It is difficult to account for the origin of this belief. Possibly it is connected with the idea of many ancient authors that fungi have a natural affinity for poisonous substances and readily absorb them: specimens which grew near serpent's holes, rusty nails, rotten rags, or even on trees bearing noxious fruits, were rendered harmful through imbibing deleterious substances and vapours. A poisonous fungus when cooked apparently released these and they were attracted to the silver and discoloured it. Indeed in southern Italy, where the harmful effect of neighbouring metals on a fungus is still believed in, it is customary to put a piece of metal in the water in which fungi are cooked with the notion that any poisonous substance attaches itself to the metal. Somewhat similar in kind are the tests which replace the silver spoon with onion, parsley or other vegetable; and similar in value.

Connected with these ideas is the one which considers fungi harmful, if they grow in highly manured ground, regardless of the fact that manure is the normal habitat of the form of the Field Mushroom which gave rise to the cultivated races. Several other edible fungi favour a rich substratum.

The taste of some fungi is intensely acrid, that of others very bitter, whereas that of the majority is mild. Taste, like colour and smell, is a specific character. Indeed in the large genus *Russula*, some classifications make taste a primary division. Though it is unwise to eat an acrid species uncooked, taste is no real guide to safety. None of the really dangerous fungi has a sharp taste.

No reliance should be placed on the fact that a species is nibbled by some animal or other. Rabbits, for example, are not usually affected by *Amanita phalloides*, simply because their stomach contents are able to neutralise the poison. Slugs have so different a mode of food assimilation from ours that it is absurd to rely on them as indicators: they thrive on the deadly poisonous species of *Amanita*.

All other tests are similarly useless, such as that edible fungi grow in fields and not in woods, in grass and not on or under trees, occur early in the season and so on. To know whether a species is edible or poisonous it is necessary to be able to recognise it and to learn its reputation. No rule-of-thumb method is safe. Indeed by every one of the usual tests the deadly poisonous *Amanita phalloides*, *Amanita verna* and *Amanita virosa* would be considered perfectly safe, whereas the Field Mushroom would give rise to doubts.

From earliest times there have been suggestions for rendering all toadstools safe to eat. Pliny says that 'vinegar being a nature diametrically opposed to them neutralises their dangerous qualities'. Later salt and alcohol were among the reasonable suggestions for neutralising the poison in fungi; the mixtures recommended for curing poisoning and the mithridates for immunising against poisoning were often so strange and complex that a knowledge of their constituents would be sufficient to empty a normal stomach.

In 1851 F. Gérard, a naturalist attached to the Jardin des Plantes, Paris, published the results of experiments showing that *Amanita phalloides* and other poisonous fungi can be rendered innocuous by cutting them up and macerating them in water with added vinegar and salt for two hours, then thoroughly washing, and boiling in water. At that time the fear of poisoning was so great that only the Cultivated Mushroom was allowed in Paris markets. Gérard's method had many advocates and for a time was mentioned in the Instructions to French Army Officers. It is believed that he was finally the victim of his experiments.

Fabre in an essay included in *The Life of a Fly* relates that he had never heard of even a mild case of mushroom poisoning in the thirty years he had lived at Sérignan, though the people gathered a little of everything to add to their modest alimentary resources. The custom in the district is to blanch the toadstools by bringing them to the boil in water with a little salt in it; afterwards a few rinsings in cold water and then cooking according to taste. Though he praises the method, the only harmful species Fabre mentions as having tried is *Amanita pantherina*. Blanching with or without the addition of vinegar has long been practised by country people in many parts of the world. According to Fabre fungi which have been blanched become much more digestible, there is no loss of succulence and hardly any of flavour. The precaution is unnecessary if only species known to be edible are cooked, and these are usually far more abundant than poisonous ones.

DESCRIPTION OF SPECIES

The average size of each fungus is given in inches at the
beginning of the description

PLATES I TO 5

AMANITA

The genus *Amanita* includes the three deadly species *Amanita phalloides*
(Pl. 1) *Amanita verna* and *Amanita virosa* (Pl. 2), and the two
poisonous species *Amanita muscaria* (Pl. 4) and *Amanita pantherina*
(Pl. 5). Not all members of the genus are harmful, however—
Amanita rubescens is a well-known edible species.

The name *Amanita* is the Greek Amanitai (ἀμανῖται), thought to
be derived from Mount Amanon in Cilicia. Apparently it was the
name for the Field Mushroom which grows abundantly in Greece
and is still called Amanites (ἀμανίτης) or more popularly Manitari
(μανιτάρι). When the name was first used in a generic sense, it
was applied to several edible species including the Field Mushroom,
but it has had its present significance for well over a century. The
main characters of the genus are white spores, white gills which are
more or less free with shorter intermediate ones, a ring on the stem
and a volva or wrapper which completely encloses the young
fungus. The behaviour of the volva depends on its structure. Where
it is composed mainly of thin-branched
hyphae with few rather elongated thick-
walled cells it holds together and splits
to allow the passage through it of the
cap as growth proceeds. The remains of
the volva are left as a cup at the base of
the stem, as shown in fig. 1 and in Plates
1 & 2. Though occasionally in dry weather
parts of the volva may adhere to the cap,
usually this is free from all trace of it.
When, however, the volva is composed
of few hyphae and many thick-walled
spherical cells it has not sufficient tenacity
to hold together as the cap is pressed

Fig. 1. *Amanita phalloides*.
a, early stage with volva
unbroken. b, fully open
with volva as a cup at the
base of the stem.

against it by the elongating stem and breaks into wart-like portions which remain on the cap, as shown in fig. 2 and in Plates 4 & 5.

An intermediate condition occurs in *Amanita mappa* (Pl. 3) where portions of the volva remain on the cap as irregular patches.

The base of the stem is always swollen. In species with a friable volva there is an ornamentation at the base of the stem which varies according to the amount of adhesion in the early stages of growth and the proportion of thick-walled cells (see fig. 3).

Fig. 2. *Amanita muscaria*. a, early stage with volva unbroken. b, fully open with volva torn into warts on the cup and rings of concentric scales at the base of the stem.

In the young stage a membranous veil encloses the young gills. As the cap expands the membrane is torn from the edge of the cap and remains as a ring attached to the stem; it frequently shows striations on its upper surface which are impressions left by the developing gills.

PLATE I

AMANITA PHALLOIDES   DEATH CAP
Average width of cap 3½, height of stem 4½, width of stem ⅝.

This deadly fungus is common in woods and adjoining pastures in late summer and early autumn. In its youngest stages it looks much like an egg half buried in the soil, until the outer membrane tears and the cap gradually emerges. The cap is fleshy and hemispherical at first, then finally flattens, varying in colour, usually an olivaceous green or yellowish green with a darker centre but occasionally brownish, yellow, or rarely even whitish; the skin is satiny when dry and somewhat viscid in wet weather; the surface is finely streaked with radiating dark fibrils. The gills are crowded and white, often with a greenish or yellowish reflection. The stem is whitish often with a tinge of green, solid at first, often becoming hollow, with a well-marked large white or greenish ring;

it is somewhat narrowed upwards with a striate apex and its bulbous base is surrounded by a large white or yellowish persistent volva, often greenish or yellowish within, which is free for half its length and has a lax margin. The flesh is white but shows a tinge of the colour of the cap below the readily separable skin. It is practically tasteless and without smell until it begins to decay, when it is fetid.

The differences in colour of the cap seem to depend upon conditions of growth. In dry weather the thin outer layer of the stem breaks into squamules showing the white flesh below, giving a well-marked marbled appearance. The ring remains attached to the cap for a long time; it often dries rapidly and sticks to the stem as a brownish skin.

Amanita phalloides is responsible for over 90 per cent of the recorded deaths by fungus poisoning. Moreover more than 50 per cent of the cases of poisoning are fatal; the percentage has been put so high as 90. The symptoms usually follow the same course. No discomfort is felt for ten to twelve hours, an almost diagnostic sign. Then there are sudden and intense abdominal pains with vomiting, diarrhoea and extreme thirst. Usually there is quiescence after two days, but this is the most dangerous period. The various symptoms recur in a more intense form and usually the nervous system is gradually paralysed, the liver degenerates, there is delirium, collapse and death. Other symptoms, no more pleasant, also occur and several distinct clinical forms have been recognised. If very little of the fungus has been eaten the symptoms may abate after two or three days; a surprisingly small amount, however, will cause illness and even death. Where there is recovery it is slow and there is prolonged convalescence.

Owing to the long incubation period ordinary simple measures for ridding the stomach of its contents are obviously not sufficient to remedy the harm already done.

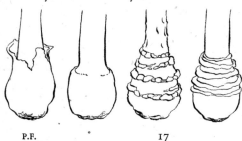

Fig. 3. Base of stem, from left to right: *Amanita phalloides, Amanita mappa, Amanita muscaria, Amanita pantherina*

The Institut Pasteur has produced an antiphalloidian serum which has given good results when injected soon after the meal, either hypodermically or intravenously in a dose of at least 40 c.c. No ill effects follow injection. Serum is produced by immunising sheep.

Based on a century-old French treatment intravenous injections of glucose (20-25 per cent) are now given in Germany, and good results are reported. The poisoning carries in its train a shortage of sugar in the blood (hypoglycaemia), probably by its effect on the liver.

A similar recent French treatment is to administer common salt solution either orally or intravenously in 20 c.c. doses of 20 per cent strength. Various physiological hypotheses have been put forward to account for the reported success of this treatment.

A treatment of a different kind consists in feeding a patient with the whole stomachs of three rabbits chopped up with the brains of seven, the assumption being that the essential poison contains two distinct portions, a toxin (hepatic) which causes degeneracy of liver and kidneys and irritates the intestine, and a toxin (neuro) which acts upon the central nervous system, bringing about progressive paralysis. The rabbit, like some other animals, is immune to small portions of the fungus, so its stomach contents must contain some substance capable of neutralising the hepatic toxin; the central nervous system of the rabbit is not affected, so it is assumed that the brain contains some antidote to the neuro-toxin. It has been said in favour of the treatment that seven rabbits are more readily procurable than serum and that these need not even be lost to the table.

Much research has been carried out to discover the poisonous principle. The first substance to be isolated was phallin, a glucoside which attacks the red corpuscles of the blood. It was assumed that this was the active poison, but it is readily destroyed by heat and by digestive juices. Moreover the symptoms of *Amanita phalloides* poisoning are not those of haemolysis. Two other substances have been isolated: Amanita-toxin (Amanitin) with a complicated and undefined chemical structure, which resists the action of heat, of drying and of the digestive juices, and phalloidin, a polypeptide, which is quickly active though destroyed by heat. Death through eating the fungus is apparently due to the heat-resistant Amanita-toxin which in experimental animals produces the majority of the lesions described in human post-mortems.

PLATE 2
AMANITA VERNA   FOOLS' MUSHROOM
Average width of cap 3, *height of stem* 5, *width of stem* $\frac{3}{8}$.

AMANITA VIROSUS   DESTROYING ANGEL
Average width of cap 5, *height of stem* $7\frac{1}{2}$, *width of stem* $\frac{5}{8}$.

Amanita verna and *Amanita virosa* are both closely allied to *Amanita phalloides* and are often regarded as varieties or sub-species. They are just as poisonous and probably more dangerous because, being white, they are more readily mistaken for Mushrooms, from which they are clearly distinguished by the persistently white gills and the membranous volva at the base of the stem, though this may be left in the ground if the specimen is gathered carelessly. Both are rare in this country.

Amanita verna closely resembles *Amanita phalloides* but is usually entirely white, though the centre of the cap may be slightly tinted ochraceous. The stem is fairly long and slender and the volva is usually more sheathing. It grows in woods, especially beech, in summer and early autumn: in spite of the specific epithet it rarely appears in spring. J. Bauhin called it *Fungus stultorum*—the fungus of fools, presumably because in its young stage it was mistaken for *Amanita caesarea.*

In *Amanita virosa* the cap is at first conical, often somewhat asymmetrical, and when expanded is always rather umbonate. The slender stem is floccosely scaly with an incomplete silky ring which is usually lower on one side and often remains attached to the edge of the cap. The volva is lax and wide. It occurs in damp woods in summer and autumn.

PLATE 3
AMANITA MAPPA   FALSE DEATH CAP
Average width of cap 3, *height of stem* $3\frac{3}{4}$, *width of stem* $\frac{1}{2}$

This species is often confused with *Amanita phalloides*. The cap, however, is usually lemon-yellow or white, with no trace of green, is without dark radiating fibrils and normally retains irregular patches of the volva: the fancied resemblance of these patches to a map accounts for the specific epithet. The chief difference is in the bulbous base of the stem, which is truncate with a short thick margin often showing the projecting torn edge of the enclosing white, yellow or brownish volva, separated from the rest of the stem by a distinct groove. The cap is fleshy, hemispherical then spread out, shiny in dry weather with white or yellow patches which become ochre or brownish. The gills are white, often with a yellowish edge, crowded and narrow. The stem is slender, solid then hollow, white or tinted yellow, and striate above the white membranous ring. The flesh is white but is often yellowish below the separable skin of the cap. It has a smell resembling that of raw potatoes and an insipid then disagreeable taste. It grows in woods, especially beech, in summer and autumn.

Until recently *Amanita mappa* was generally thought to be very poisonous. It is now known to be harmless, though worthless because of its offensive flavour.

PLATE 4

AMANITA MUSCARIA   FLY AGARIC

Average width of cap 7, height of stem 10, width of stem 1

This beautiful fungus is well known, for not only is it conspicuous and common in woodlands in autumn, but it often figures in nursery pictures, as table decorations, in films such as *Fantasia* and serves as a model for children's toys. The cap is scarlet or orange-red, slightly viscid, shiny and dotted with thick white or yellowish wart-like patches which are often arranged more or less concentrically; roundish when young, it expands until it is flat with a striate edge. The crowded gills are white or tinted with yellow, thick, with a minutely toothed edge. The stem is white or tinted yellow, stuffed then hollow, often scaly, striate above the ring, nearly cylindrical except for the bulbous base which is encircled by several more or less distinct zones of white or yellowish squamules: the ring is white or edged with yellow. The flesh is white except under the separable skin of the cap where it is orange-yellow. The taste is pleasant and there is no appreciable smell. It grows mostly under birches but also occurs under pines. When conditions are damp the cap may slip through the volva without tearing it and is then without spots.

The specific epithet *muscaria* refers to the fact first mentioned by Albertus Magnus, in the 13th century, that the fungus broken up in milk kills flies. In country districts on the Continent the method is still used, though in Poland and Czechoslovakia sugar solution replaces milk, or sugar is sprinkled on the cap. In Rumania the fungus is frequently placed on window-sills to discourage flies from entering. It was formerly employed in this country and in Sweden for getting rid of bugs, which accounts for the name Bug Agaric which is occasionally met with.

Amongst the Koryak tribes of north-east Siberia the fungus is eaten to produce a state of excessive emotion on occasions which seem to warrant it. For over two centuries it has been known that to prolong the festivities use is made of the fact that the stimulant is eliminated by the kidneys. According to Scandinavian tradition the Vikings ate *Amanita muscaria* to go berserk. It figures in homoeopathy as Agaricus or Aga formerly as one of the antipsorics.

Though popularly regarded as the most poisonous toadstool, *Amanita muscaria* never causes death in healthy people. Usually one to three hours or so after a meal there is a period of delirium and hallucinations, sometimes accompanied by intestinal disturbances. After a few hours this is followed by intense stupor and an awakening to complete forgetfulness.

The poison resides principally in the skin of the cap, but there is good evidence of considerable variation in the amount present. The fungus is eaten in some regions apparently without ill effect; but the price in the barren Steppes, three or four reindeer for a single specimen, suggests considerable potency.

The first poison to be isolated was muscarine (myco-muscarine) which is present in small amounts. It has well-marked effects but they are not those characteristic of poisoning by *Amanita muscaria*. Later another alkaloid was isolated which, because its effects on the central nervous system are similar to those produced by atropine, is usually called mycetoatropine (muscaridine) though its precise chemical constitution is not known. A third alkaloid, choline, occurs in fairly large amounts and is probably responsible for the gastrointestinal symptoms which sometimes occur.

PLATE 5
AMANITA PANTHERINA FALSE BLUSHER
Average width of cap 4, height of stem 5, width of stem ½

This species is liable to be confused with the edible *Amanita rubescens*, but the flesh and gills do not redden, the cap is always some shade of brown with numerous small white warts and the base of the stem is surrounded by circular remnants of the volva.

The cap is convex then spread out, fleshy, brownish grey, brown or yellowish brown and darker in the centre; it is a little viscid when damp and shiny when dry and has a striate edge. The gills are white and crowded. The stem is white, stuffed then hollow, often narrower and striate above, and the bulbous base is surrounded by a membranous border with one or more scaly bracelets above it which are the remains of the volva; the ring is attached obliquely about the middle of the stem and is thin and often fugaceous. The flesh is white with a slight smell of radish and a mild taste. It grows in woods, heaths and pastures in summer and autumn.

Amanita pantherina is poisonous. The symptoms are similar to those produced by *Amanita muscaria* but are apparently more serious.

PLATE 6
LEPIOTA HELVEOLA POISONOUS LEPIOTA
Average width of cap 1¼, height of stem 1½, width of stem ¼

LEPIOTA CRISTATA CRESTED LEPIOTA
Average width of cap 1½, height of stem 5½, width of stem 3/16

There are a number of small species of *Lepiota* which are brownish with an admixture of pink. All are rare in this country, and there is still uncertainty about their specific differences. As, however, one or more of them cause symptoms resembling mild *Amanita phalloides* poisoning, an inclusive description is given.

Lepiota helveola has a rounded then flattened cap, sometimes with a slight central prominence, at first covered with an ochre-brown cuticle which becomes flushed with pink or lilac-colour especially in damp weather and tears, except on the disk, into numerous scales showing a white or pinkish surface between. The gills are white, then cream-colour, crowded and have a fimbriate edge. The stem is cylindrical, hollow, concolorous with the cap and covered with silky fibrils; the ring is in the form of an annular bracelet. The flesh is white, often becoming slightly pinkish when cut, with a pleasant smell and a sourish taste. It grows amongst grass in autumn.

Lepiota cristata has the cap at first campanulate and covered with a brownish or reddish brown cuticle; later, as the cap becomes convex, the cuticle breaks up except in the centre, where there is usually a boss, and shows as concentric circles of small scales looking as if they were encrusted in a white satiny surface. The gills are white or whitish, crowded, thin and attached to a sort of collarette which separates them from the stem. The slender hollow stem is white and silky and often tinged with pink or yellow, especially towards the base, from which white branching mycelial fibres spread in the soil; the ring is membranous, white and fugaceous. The flesh is white, the taste unpleasant and the smell strong and disagreeable. It grows from spring to autumn in grassy places.

Because of the disagreeable smell and unpleasant taste *Lepiota cristata* is usually considered suspect. It is not poisonous.

PLATE 7

LACTARIUS TORMINOSUS   WOOLLY MILK CAP
Average width of cap 6, height of stem 2, width of stem 1

In this species the milk is white and has a very acrid taste. The cap is convex at first with the strongly inrolled margin hiding the gills and covered with a whitish woolly felt; later, on expansion, it becomes depressed in the middle; it is viscid when moist and is usually rosy pink or pale orange-red, though it may be almost white, with darker concentric zones and a paler margin. The gills are thin, decurrent and yellowish pink. The stem is coloured like the cap but paler and sometimes has small superficial pits; it is firm and brittle and finally becomes hollow. The flesh is pinkish. It occurs in summer and autumn in woods and on heaths, frequently under birches.

Lactarius torminosus is not really poisonous, though, like all acrid species of *Lactarius*, it acts as an irritant when eaten raw—*torminosus* means griping. Cooking destroys the acrid principle. It is the favourite toadstool in Finland, where it is boiled in water, eaten at once or salted down. It is eaten also in neighbouring countries. In Norway it is strongly roasted and added to coffee.

PLATE 8

RUSSULA EMETICA   SICKENER
Average width of cap 4, height of stem 3, width of stem 1

RUSSULA FRAGILIS   FRAGILE RUSSULA
Average width of cap 2¾, height of stem 2, width of stem ⅜

RUSSULA FELLEA   BITTER RUSSULA
Average width of cap 4, height of stem 2½, width of stem ¾

RUSSULA DRIMEIA   PUNGENT RUSSULA
Average width of cap 4, height of stem 3, width of stem ¾

The genus *Russula* much resembles *Lactarius* but no milk is exuded when the brittle flesh is broken. Many of the species are brightly coloured. Most have a mild taste and are edible. Others have an acrid taste and are usually considered poisonous; though whatever irritant substance they may contain is dispersed in cooking, they are best avoided.

Russula emetica has a cap convex then flattened or depressed, pink then a shiny bright red, but readily losing colour and fading to pink, yellow or white: the edge is at first smooth but later becomes furrowed; the skin is easily removed. The gills are shining white, more or less free and somewhat crowded. The stem is rigid and white or tinted pink. The flesh is firm and white, pink under the skin of the cap. The taste is very acrid after a few seconds and persistent; the smell is pleasant. It occurs in woods in summer and autumn, different forms being associated with beeches and conifers.

Russula fragilis much resembles *Russula emetica*, but though the cap is typically bright red there is a much wider range of colour.

It is usually smaller and the cap has a striate edge. The stem is spongy then hollow, and very fragile. The flesh is not pink under the skin of the cap. The taste is immediately very acrid and is not so durable: the smell is pleasant. It occurs in woods in summer and autumn. The commonest form has a red cap. Some colour forms have been given varietal names.

Russula fellea is entirely pale ochraceous. The cap is convex then flattened, viscid, the centre darker, the margin thin and striate. The gills are adnate, thin and somewhat crowded, and are white at first and exude watery drops. The stem is cylindrical, white, then the colour of the cap but paler. The flesh is firm, whitish then pale ochraceous. The taste is very acrid and bitter, the smell pleasant. It grows in beech woods in late summer and autumn.

Russula drimeia has a bright purple or brown-violet cap, darker in the middle, and decoloured by rain; it is convex with an incurved margin then flat or depressed, a little viscid. The gills are adnate and somewhat crowded, citron-yellow then sulphur-yellow. The stem is solid and firm, concolorous with the cap but paler. The flesh is compact, yellowish then white, purplish under the skin. The taste is very acrid and the smell pleasant. It grows in coniferous woods in autumn.

There is a variety (*Queletii*) which has white gills.

PLATE 9

ENTOLOMA LIVIDUM   LEADEN ENTOLOMA
Average width of cap 5, height of stem 3, width of stem 1

The genus *Entoloma* has pink spores and, typically, sinuate gills.

The cap in *Entoloma lividum* is tawny or greyish, often turning white here and there: it is hard and compact, roundish and regular at first with a thin, mealy, strongly inrolled edge, and then flattened, except for the central fleshy disk, with the edge becoming irregularly raised; the skin is finely silky. The gills are yellowish then pink, often with a yellow edge. The stem is shining white, and firm, somewhat swollen above or below; the apex is mealy and there are fine striations on its surface. The white fragile flesh has first an agreeable smell and taste of meal, but the pleasantness is not lasting. It grows in grassy places in autumn, especially in deciduous woods.

It often causes violent sickness and diarrhoea, and occasional death. It is known about Dijon as 'le grand empoisonneur de la Côte d'Or'.

PLATE 10

HEBELOMA CRUSTULINIFORME
CRUSTLIKE HEBELOMA
Average width of cap 4¼, height of stem 2¼, width of stem 1

VOLVARIA GLOIOCEPHALA   STICKY VOLVARIA
Average width of cap 4½, height of stem 7, width of stem ½

The genus *Hebeloma* has brown spores and, typically, sinuate gills.

Hebeloma crustuliniforme has the cap convex, then spread out with often a flattened central boss and a thin undulating edge; it is pale yellow, brown or reddish, darker in the centre, and at first viscid. The gills are white then clay-coloured, and finally date-brown, crowded and with an uneven edge: in wet weather, or after heavy dew, drops of liquid are exuded from the gill edges and show as spots on drying. The whitish stem is short, stuffed then hollow and often thickened at the base; the apex has white squamules which become coloured brownish when covered with the falling spores. The flesh is white and firm and has the smell and taste of radish. Often growing in rings in grassy places in woods in autumn, it suggests a row of rolls coming from a baker's oven—hence *crustu-liniforme*.

Hebeloma crustuliniforme is very indigestible, and the persistent taste of radish after cooking makes it objectionable.

The genus *Volvaria* has pink spores, free gills and a membranous volva.

In *Volvaria gloiocephala* the cap is first campanulate and finally spread out but with a central prominence; it is glutinous, and is entirely smoky grey, or white with the disk greyish, and has a striate edge. The gills are crowded, white and then salmon-pink. The

26

stem is white, later often grey or tawny, at first mealy, cylindrical but usually narrowed above and swollen at the base and surrounded by the white or grey persistent volva. The flesh is soft and white with an unpleasant taste and smell. It grows in grass usually on heaps of rubbish, straw or manure in summer and autumn; occasionally on thatched roofs and on vegetable remains in sand dunes.

Formerly this species was regarded as deadly poisonous. It is harmless and is much eaten in Portugal and Algeria.

PLATE 11

INOCYBE PATOUILLARDI
RED STAINING INOCYBE
Average width of cap 2, height of stem 3½, width of stem ½

INOCYBE GEOPHYLLA   EARTHY INOCYBE
Average width of cap ¾, height of stem 2, width of stem $\frac{1}{16}$

In the genus *Inocybe* the surface of the cap is usually covered with radiating fibrils or is somewhat scaly: the spores are dull brown. Most species are small, some are poisonous and none is known to be edible.

Inocybe Patouillardi is at first wholly creamy white, then becomes pinky yellow and finally more or less completely vermilion or brownish red: in the young stage it immediately stains red on handling as in the drawings which were of specimens bruised in the post. The cap is fleshy, conical, campanulate at first with an inrolled margin, covered with silky fibrils; later it flattens out but retains an acute boss in the centre, and the margin may become lobed and torn. The gills are almost free, crowded, whitish pink then rusty brown or olivaceous with a white floccose edge, becoming blotched with red. The stem is rather stout, solid, slightly swollen at the base, mealy at the top. The flesh is firm and white and reddens slightly, particularly in the stem. The smell is rather strong and fruity and the taste is mild. It occurs in summer in deciduous woods, especially beech. There are several species of *Inocybe* which redden on touching and it is very difficult to distinguish between them except on microscopic characters.

Inocybe Patouillardi has caused occasional deaths. There was a fatality in Surrey in 1937: others who partook of the fungus in a more reasonable manner had giddiness then profuse sweats and vomiting. Some soldiers who ate what was probably this fungus in 1925 had the same symptoms though not all suffered ill effects. The poisoning is of the *Amanita muscaria* type.

In *Inocybe geophylla* the silky fibrillose cap is conical with an inrolled margin then spread out with a central boss; it is of varied colour, white, yellowish, fawn, reddish, lilac or blue, often with the centre a different colour. The gills are crowded, usually free, at first whitish and finally pale ochraceous. The stem is whitish, or a paler colour than the cap, solid and firm, satiny, with a mealy apex and slightly thickened base. The flesh is white, the smell earthy and the taste insipid. It occurs in woods from late summer to winter.

The lilac-coloured specimens are var. *lilacina*. The colour is lost after a day or so in darkness but is regained with exposure to light.

Inocybe geophylla is often said to be poisonous but there is no definite information about it.

PLATE 12

PSALLIOTA XANTHODERMA
YELLOW STAINING MUSHROOM

Average width of cap 3½, height of stem 4, width of stem ¾

This is a true mushroom: it has purple-brown spores, free gills and a ring on the stem.

The skin instantly becomes bright yellow where touched or rubbed, and the flesh at the base of the stem shows the same colour when cut or broken: the yellow changes gradually to brown. The cap is at first bell-shaped but flattened in the middle, becoming convex and finally spread out; it is usually pure white with a silky sheen. The gills are crowded, at first white then, after a time, pinkish and finally purple-brown. The stem is long, cylindrical, flexuous, and swollen into a well-marked bulbous base; it is white and silky, at first floccose within, then hollow, with a thin, membranous white ring. The flesh generally is white, the taste strong, the smell usually unpleasant. It grows, often in circles, in pastures, hedgerows and woodlands in summer and autumn.

Though not poisonous it is very indigestible and causes illness in some people.

Varieties occur which have the cap more or less scaly.

The Horse Mushroom (*Psalliota arvensis*) often has patches of yellow on the cap and stem but the colour is permanent and much duller than in *Psalliota xanthoderma*.

PLATE 13

BOLETUS SATANAS   DEVIL'S BOLETUS

Average width of cap 6, height of stem 3, width of stem 3

This most handsome *Boletus* has a dirty white or greyish cap often with a tinge of olive, smooth and soft to the touch, at first hemispherical with the thin inrolled margin reaching the stem, then more flattened. The tubes are yellow or greenish yellow, short and almost free from the stem; the pores are rather small and rounded, at first yellow, then bright crimson though sometimes remaining yellow at the margin. The short swollen stem is usually yellow above and below, and bright red in the middle; it is covered with a close network of bright red veins which become laxer and paler below. The flesh is white or yellowish white and reddens in the stem and cap when exposed to the air and then slowly becomes bluish green. The taste is mild and the smell slight. It occurs in late summer in woods, heaths and pastures on chalky soil.

All parts of the fungus turn blue when rubbed.

Boletus Satanas was so called because when first described over a century ago it had caused sickness and diarrhoea in several who ate it, or merely tasted it, and even by emanations given off from specimens that were being examined. Though it may be that there are differences in the toxicity of this species, its powers of evil have been much overrated. It is probably very indigestible and may contain some irritant substance. It is eaten in Czechoslovakia and in parts of Italy, but there is general agreement that it should not be eaten raw.

PLATE 14

BOLETUS LURIDUS   LURID BOLETUS
Average width of cap 4, height of stem 4, width of stem 1¾

BOLETUS ERYTHROPUS DOTTED STEM BOLETUS
Average width of cap 3, height of stem 3, width of stem 1½

Boletus luridus is frequently mistaken for *Boletus Satanas*, but the cap is some shade of brown and never whitish, and the pores are orange-red or red-brown.

The cap varies in colour with weather conditions and age from olive-brown when young to umber, reddish brown, or buff; it is fleshy, thick, hemispherical then convex and finely velvety. The tubes are yellow, becoming blue or green when old; they are free and shorter at the margin and near the stem so that there is a circular depression; the small rounded pores are yellow when young, changing to red-brown or orange-red and turn blackish blue when bruised. The stem is short and swollen at first but becomes elongated and more or less cylindrical; it is yellow at the summit, washed with red elsewhere, browning at the base, and ornamented with a blood-red network. The flesh is thick and soft, yellow except for a reddish zone under the tubes and at the base of the stem; when broken it rapidly becomes blue after a momentary violet-red stage, and, later, yellowish green. The taste is mild and the smell feeble. It grows in woods from summer to late autumn, and in heaths and pastures.

Boletus erythropus is very similar to *Boletus luridus*, but its stem is covered with reddish dots, the flesh is clear yellow under the tubes, and the cap is usually darker brown and finely tomentose. It grows usually in coniferous woods.

Both species are edible. The rapid change of colour when the flesh is broken is doubtless responsible for the widespread belief that they are very poisonous. The flesh becomes yellow during cooking.

PLATE 15

BOLETUS FELLEUS   BITTER BOLETUS
Average width of cap 4½, height of stem 4, width of stem 1

When young, and the tubes still white, this species is sometimes confused with *Boletus edulis*. The network on the stem is, however, more marked, and the taste is so bitter as to have been described as unforgettable. Mature specimens are distinguished at once by the pink tubes and pores. The cap is pale yellowish, honey- or chestnut-colour, hemispherical then flattened, and slightly pubescent. The tubes are adnate and, like the angular pores, first white then pink. The cylindric stem is a little paler than the cap and is covered with a network which is very fine and whitish at the apex and widens below towards the swollen base, becoming chestnut-brown and finally blackish. The white flesh becomes pinkish when cut. It grows in woods, especially on calcareous soil, in summer and autumn. Though not poisonous its intensely bitter taste renders it inedible; a single specimen will ruin a meal.

PLATE 16

CLAVARIA FORMOSA   HANDSOME CLAVARIA
Height 5, width 6

GYROMITRA ESCULENTA   GYROMITRA
Average width of cap 5, height of stem 2, width of stem 2

Many species of *Clavaria* are club-shaped growing singly (fairy clubs), or tufted at the base. Other species are branched (coral fungi); one of the most handsome of these is *Clavaria formosa*, a very rare fungus in this country, occurring in woods, especially under beech, in summer and autumn, usually forming rings.

The base of the fungus is short and stout, white at first then a pinkish buff. Above this there is repeated branching which shows little sign of regularity; the branches are elongated and erect, roundish or flattened, and clearly grooved, orange- or salmon-pink, then ochraceous with divided blunt yellow or pinkish yellow tips. The flesh is white and very fragile with a slightly acrid taste and a pleasant smell.

Clavaria formosa is usually regarded as edible but it often causes purging.

Gyromitra is an Ascomycete closely related to the Morels (*Morchella*). The cap of *Gyromitra esculenta* is fawn then dark chestnut-brown, and characteristically brain-like owing to the surface being irregularly folded and grooved and turned in on to the stem, to which it is joined here and there. The stem is whitish, smooth, flattened, grooved, sometimes branched above. Both cap and stem show irregular cavities when sectioned. The flesh is white, waxy and very brittle with a pleasant taste and smell. It grows in coniferous woods throughout the spring, often appearing under the snow, particularly in burnt or open places; also in the flat wet 'slacks' of sand dunes.

Gyromitra esculenta is perfectly safe when cooked or dried but has caused serious accidents and even death when eaten raw. The poisoning is usually attributed to helvellic acid which acts on the red blood-corpuscles, and the symptoms recorded for earlier cases support this view. However, numerous poisonings, particularly in Germany, have shown that the action is not simple haemolysis, but its true nature still remains in doubt. Large quantities of the raw fungus are exported annually from Poland principally to Germany. The factory workers suffer from eye trouble either from the spores of the fungus or from irritation by poison on the fingers.

BIBLIOGRAPHY

The standard work on the larger fungi is Carleton Rea, *British Basidiomycetae*, Cambridge, 1922. An introductory book with some coloured plates is E. W. Swanton, *Fungi and how to know them*, Methuen, 2nd ed. 1923. The only full treatment of poisoning is in J. Ramsbottom, *A Handbook of the Larger British Fungi*, British Museum (Natural History), 1923 [Photofacsimile, 1944]. *Edible and Poisonous Fungi*, Ministry of Agriculture and Fisheries, Bulletin No. 23. 4th ed. (reprinted 1939) has coloured plates. J. Ramsbottom, *Fungi*, Benns' Sixpenny Library, 1929, is an introduction to Mycology, and *Mushrooms and Toadstools*, Collins, 1946, with kodachrome photographs is a general account.

Amanita phalloides

2

Amanita verna (a)   *Amanita virosa* (b)

Amanita mappa

Amanita muscaria

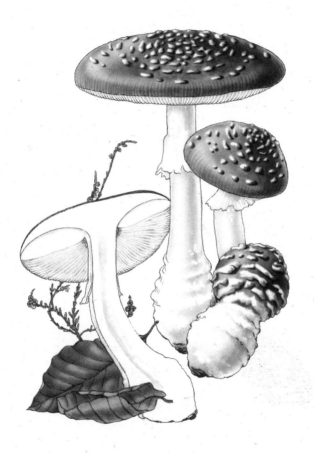

Amanita pantherina

Lepiota helveola (a)   Lepiota cristata (b)

Lactarius torminosus

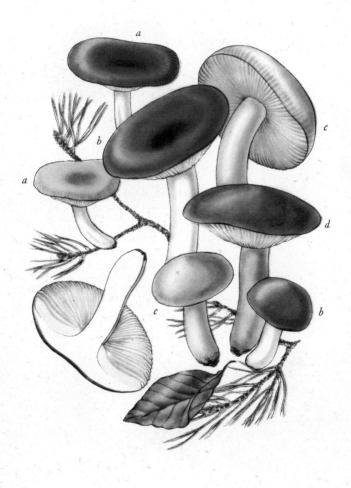

Russula fragilis (a)   *Russula fellea (c)*
Russula emetica (b)   *Russula drimeia (d)*

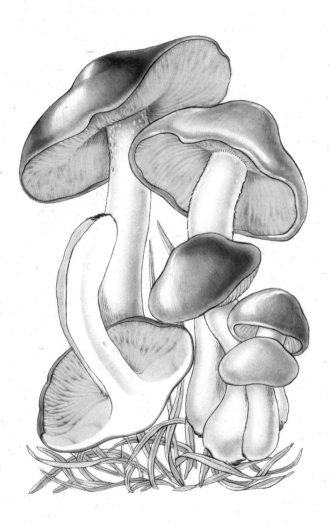

Entoloma lividum

Hebeloma crustuliniforme (a)   *Volvaria gloiocephala* (b)

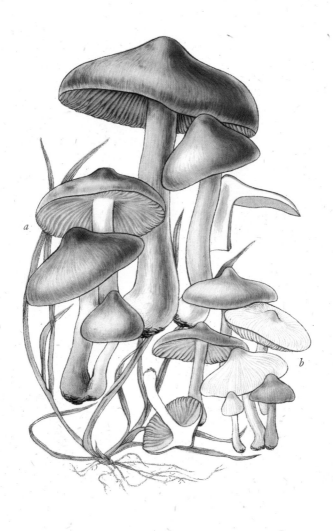

Inocybe Patouillardi (*a*) *Inocybe geophylla* (*b*)

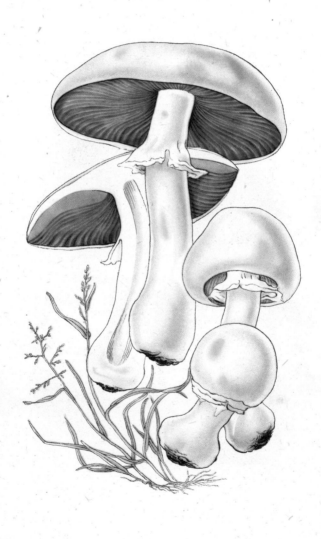

Psalliota xanthoderma

Boletus Satanas

Boletus luridus (a)   *Boletus erythropus* (b)

Boletus felleus

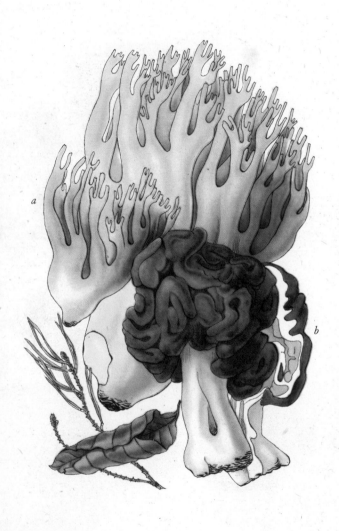

Clavaria formosa (*a*) *Gyromitra esculenta* (*b*)